a gift for

_____

from

_____

When Santa learned the Gospel

Written by Simon Camilleri

Illustrated by Matt Boutros

10 Publishing
a division of 10 of those.com

Dedicated with gratitude
to those elves who shared the gospel with us.

For my daughter, Dorothy.

Copyright © 2017 by Simon Camilleri

First published in Great Britain in 2017

The right of Simon Camilleri to be identified as the Author of this Work has been asserted by him in accordance with the Copyright, Designs and Patents Act 1988.

British Library Cataloguing in Publication Data
A record for this book is available from the British Library

ISBN: 978-1-911272-89-2

Illustrated by Matt Boutros

Printed in Turkey

10Publishing, a division of 10ofthose.com
Unit C, Tomlinson Road, Leyland, PR25 2DY, England
Email: info@10ofthose.com
Website: www.10ofthose.com

For more information about this book go to www.santagospel.com

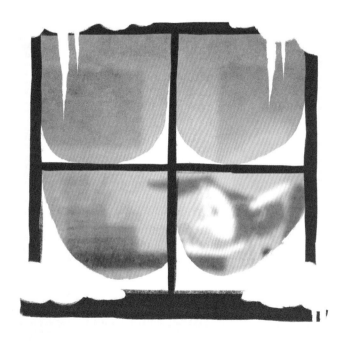

When Santa learned the gospel, he first heard it from an elf.
This tiny Santa's helper had just learned of it herself.

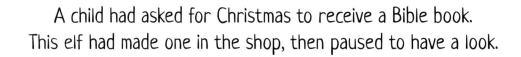

A child had asked for Christmas to receive a Bible book.
This elf had made one in the shop, then paused to have a look.

She read all about Jesus and the call to follow him.
She learned how Jesus lived
and taught
and died to pay for sin.

She learned how Jesus rose again
and how he will return,
and then this elf read how she should respond to all she'd learned.

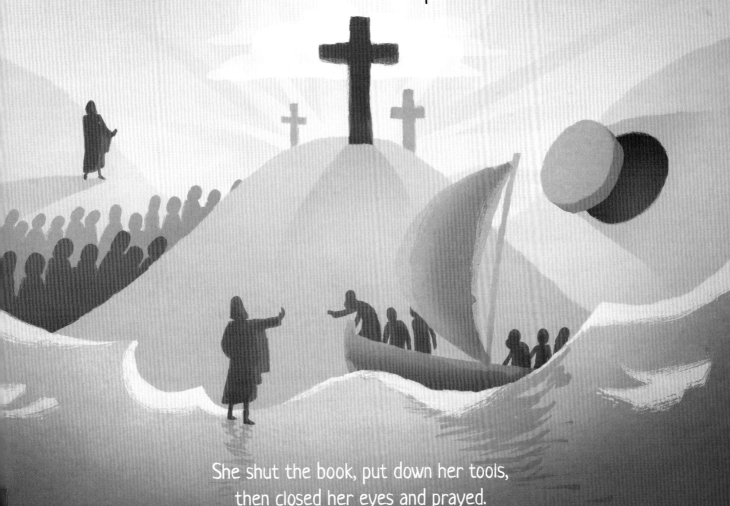

She shut the book, put down her tools,
then closed her eyes and prayed.
Right then and there this little elf trusted in Christ that day.

The next day she told Santa. It was awkward, unprepared.
She knew she didn't know that much, but what she knew, she shared.

She told Santa the gospel.
It was simple. It was short.

But a seed was sown in Santa's heart,
which grew
into
a thought.

Santa reflected on his life and the message he supported,
then compared it to the gospel that the elf had just reported.

He'd always thought that everyone was naughty or was nice.
He had them all on two big lists. He even checked it twice.

He'd always thought you only got a gift if you'd been good.
The naughty kids got lumps of coal. That's what he understood.

They'd all line up in shopping malls and sit upon his knee
and claim that they were always nice. As nice as nice can be.

Of course, he saw them when they slept and knew when they awoke.
He also knew their "nice attempts" were pretty much a joke.

Their heads weren't filled with thoughts as nice as kindness, peace and joy,
but with the never-ending list of their desired toys.

He knew their hearts, but he had thought, "They're trying to be good.
That's good enough to make the list. Otherwise no one would!"

So every year their "good enough" with toys would be rewarded.
And every year (he realised)
        this message he supported:

THE "GOOD" WILL GET THE PRESENTS
THE "BAD" WILL GET THE COAL
AND TRYING TO BE GOOD ENOUGH
IS GOOD ENOUGH A GOAL

COAL

That was the message that he knew, but now he knew another.
He had just learned the gospel.
So he compared them to each other.

The message of the gospel turned his message upside down.

The good, the bad, naughty and nice,

it switched it all around.

NAUGHTY

"There's no one good but God alone"
he'd heard Jesus concluded,
and those who claim they're "good enough"
are simply just deluded.

If there's a list of who is "good",
that standard
we've all missed,

and Santa saw that even he was on the naughty list.

That shook his world.

That rocked his boat.

That gripped him in his soul!

To think that even Santa Claus
deserved a lump of coal!

But that was only half of what
the gospel message said.
It also flipped what happened
to the naughty on its head...

Instead of being written off as just not good enough,
the message to the naughty list was one of grace and love.

The gospel offered mercy
to all those deserving coal.

The gospel offered forgiveness
and cleansing of the soul.

The gospel told how Jesus died our death to pay the price.
To reconcile us all to God – both naughty and the nice.

This offer was a real gift,
unlike presents 'neath the tree.

It was not earned by being good.
God offered it for free.

Santa compared his message with this new one he had learned.
His message said you got the presents your good deeds had earned.

The message of the gospel
offered something so much greater...

Jesus had come to reconcile the world
to their Creator.

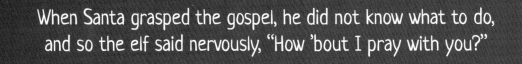

When Santa grasped the gospel, he did not know what to do,
and so the elf said nervously, "How 'bout I pray with you?"

So that night at the North Pole, by the fire in his den,
with a simple prayer led by an elf,
Santa was born again.

And now, in Christ, forgiven, free
his new life had begun

and Santa had a new message to share with everyone.

Happy Christmas

Tricky Words Glossary

There may be some words in the story that you or your kids are not familiar with.
You'll find here a short definition as well as a Bible reference in brackets, so that you can see where these words are talked about in the Bible.

Bible   A very special book that God has given to us. It tells the story of God's relationship with people and the whole book points to the gospel about Jesus.
(2 Timothy 3:15–17)

Gospel   The good news about who Jesus is and what he has done to reconcile us to God. The word "gospel" means "good news".
(1 Corinthians 15:1–5)

God   The one who made everything and everyone. God is the most wise, powerful, good and loving being that exists. There is only one God but within God there are three persons – the Father, the Son and the Holy Spirit.
(Acts 17:24–25)

Jesus   The name given to God the Son when he became a human. "Jesus" means "God Saves", because Jesus saves us from our sin by dying for us on the cross.
(Matthew 1:20–25)

Christ   This is not Jesus' last name. "Christ" means the same as "Messiah". It is the title of the special king that God promised would come.
(John 4:25–26)

Sin   To turn away from God in your heart, mind or actions.
(Isaiah 53:6)

Mercy   When God doesn't give us the punishment for our sin that we deserve.
(Ephesians 2:3–5)

Grace   When God shows us kindness that we don't deserve.
(Ephesians 2:6–9)

Forgiveness   When God deletes our record of sin so we can be reconciled to God.
(Colossians 2:13–14)

Reconcile   When we go from being God's enemy to God's friend.
(Colossians 1:19–22)

Prayer   Speaking to God.
(Matthew 6:5–13)

Creator   Another title for God, because God created everything including us.
(Genesis 1:1–31)

Born Again   To be given new life by God. To be adopted into God's family forever.
(John 3:3–8)

Why not look up the references in the Bible to learn more about these tricky words?

The Author's Inspiration

The inspiration for this book came around Christmas 2013 after I witnessed an amusing moment during a local community carols event. After we'd sung everything from "O Holy Night" to "Santa Claus is Coming to Town", the time came for Santa to come out. As expected, he asked the crowd of excited children, "So, who's been a good boy or girl this year?" "Meeeeeee!!" they all screamed. Then he asked cheekily, "And who's been a naughty boy or girl?" To his surprise, the kids again screamed, "Meeeeee!!". After an awkward moment, Santa shrugged and said, "Oh well... I guess you've tried to be good", proceeding then to randomly throw out presents to the expectant crowd.

What a message, I thought! A weird mix of moralism and apathy – of "only good people get a gift" and "everyone is pretty much a good person". I thought about how so many believe that's what Christianity teaches. The truth is, the message of the gospel is exactly the opposite. In contrast to the "good people go to heaven" idea, Jesus taught that everyone needs mercy and he had come to die for sinners like you and me – to bring the gift of forgiveness to all who would trust in him.

These truths had transformed my life and so I left that community carols event reflecting on the various messages we teach our kids and ourselves, and musing about the contrast between Jesus' message and Santa's. That's when I got this funny idea. What would happen if the character of Santa heard about the gospel? Would he find it challenging? How might he respond?

It has been a joy to collaborate with Matt Boutros to turn this idea into a beautifully illustrated Children's book. I hope you find it fun and engaging as you read it with your kids and reflect on how the messages we believe compare to Jesus' gospel of grace.

Thank you

to Jesus (who the gospel is all about),
to my amazing wife Catherine,
to Matt my friend and illustrator,
to my enthusiastic friends, family
and supportive church community
and to you, for reading this far.

(Philippians 1:3–5)

For more resources
or to find out more about this book:

www.SantaGospel.com